Rhythm and Rhyme

Senior Authors

Roger C. Farr

Dorothy S. Strickland

Authors

Richard F. Abrahamson ♦ Alma Flor Ada ♦ Barbara Bowen Coulter
Bernice E. Cullinan ♦ Margaret A. Gallego
W. Dorsey Hammond
Nancy Roser ♦ Junko Yokota ♦ Hallie Kay Yopp

Senior Consultant

Asa G. Hilliard III

Consultants

V. Kanani Choy ♦ Lee Bennett Hopkins ♦ Stephen Krashen ♦ Rosalia Salinas

Harcourt Brace & Company

Orlando Atlanta Austin Boston San Francisco Chicago Dallas New York Toronto London

All rights reserved. No part of this publication may be reproduced or transmitted in any form or by any means, electronic or mechanical, including photocopy, recording, or any information storage and retrieval system, without permission in writing from the publisher.

Requests for permission to make copies of any part of the work should be mailed to: Permissions Department, Harcourt Brace & Company, 6277 Sea Harbor Drive, Orlando, Florida 32887-6777.

HARCOURT BRACE and Quill Design is a registered trademark of Harcourt Brace & Company.

Acknowledgments appear in the back of this work.

Printed in the United States of America

ISBN 0-15-306413-7

4 5 6 7 8 9 10   048   99 98 97

Dear Reader,

You probably already know that books can be a lot of fun — you can meet new friends, visit new places, and learn new things. But did you know that books can be even *more* fun if the words in them have **rhythm and rhyme!**

As you read the stories in this book, the rhythm and the rhyme will have you clapping, tapping, and reading along! So, come on! Let's have fun!

Sincerely,

The Authors
The Authors

CONTENTS

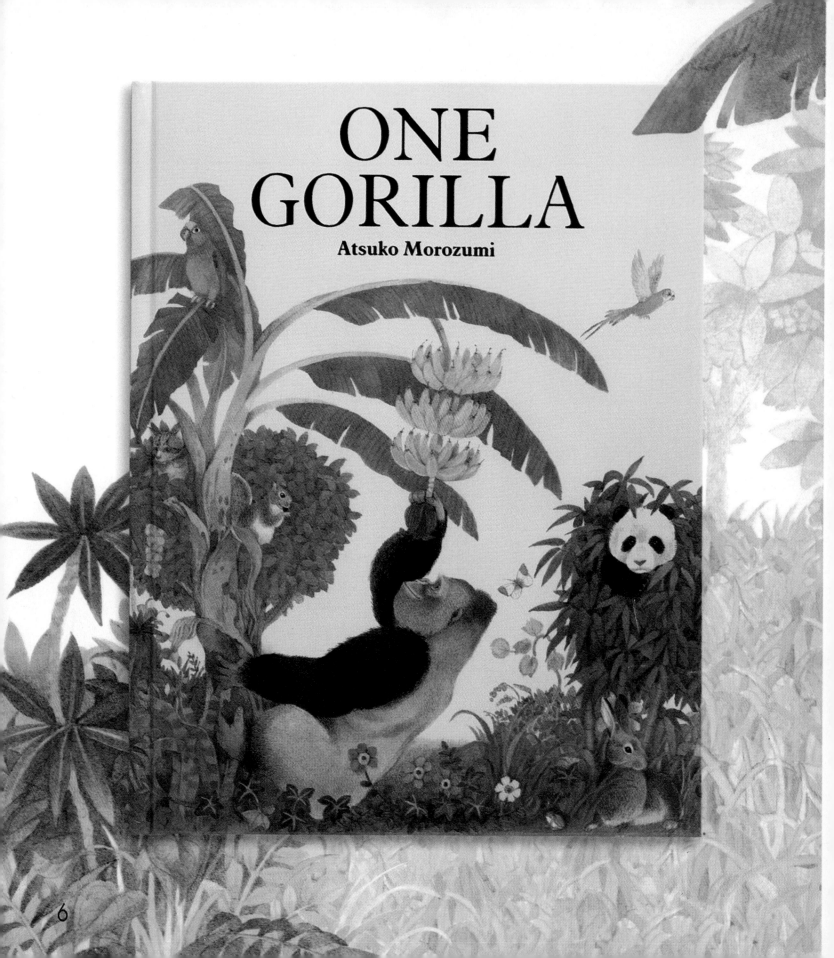

ONE
GORILLA

Atsuko Morozumi

Here is a list of things I love.
One gorilla.

Two butterflies among the flowers
and one gorilla.

Three parakeets in my house
and one gorilla.

13

Four squirrels in the woods
and one gorilla.

Five pandas in the snow
and one gorilla.

Six rabbits in a field
and one gorilla.

Seven frogs by the fence
and one gorilla.

Eight fish in the sea
and one gorilla.

Nine birds among the leaves
and one gorilla.

Ten cats in my garden
and one gorilla.

10 cats

9 birds

8 fish

7 frogs

6 rabbits

5 pandas

4 squirrels

3 parakeets

2 butterflies

But where is my gorilla?

Ah, there he is.

31

Small friends
Tall friends

Playing-soccerball friends

Talk friends

Chalk friends

Come-and-take-a-walk friends

Wriggly friends
Squiggly friends
Laughing and giggly friends

Riding friends
Gliding friends

Seeking-and-hiding friends

Bumble friends
Humble friends

Toss, turn, and tumble friends

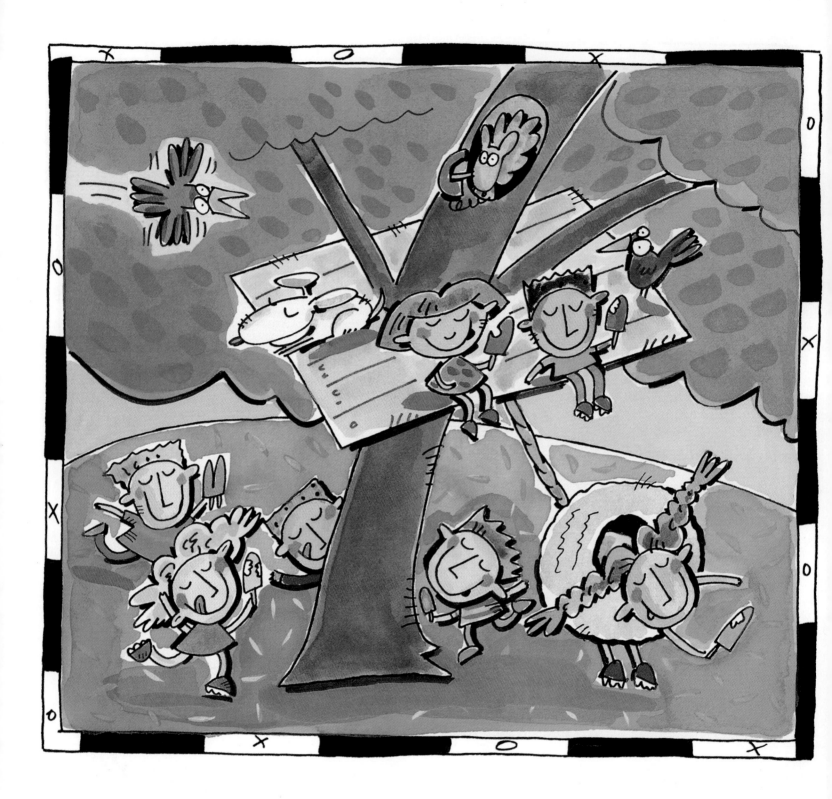

Eating friends
Treating friends
Calling-a-meeting friends

Glad friends
Sad friends

Please-don't-be-mad friends

School friends
Jewel friends
Lounging-by-the-pool friends

Witty friends
Kitty friends
Living-in-the-city friends

51

Joy friends
Toy friends
Singing girl-and-boy friends

Light friends
Bright friends
Glow-white-at-night friends

Bug friends
Snug friends

Sharing-a-warm-hug friends

Young friends
Old friends
Hot friends
Cold friends

59

All-kinds-of-weather friends

Always-together friends!

Skip to My Lou

Illustrated by Debbie Tilley

Riding in a big bus,
Painted blue.
Good-bye to the city,
And school, too.

We're off to the farm!
Hurray! Ya-HOO!

Skip to my Lou, my darling!

Good morning, Farmer,
How are you?
Walk with your partners,
Two by two.

Don't get lost, or
What will we do?
Skip to my Lou, my darling!

Cows in the barnyard,
Moo, cows, moo.
Pigs, ducks, sheep,
And horses, too.

Hens and roosters,
Cock-a-doodle-do.
Skip to my Lou, my darling!

Close that gate,
And the barn door, too!
Look! All the animals
Are going through!

Oh, my goodness!
What did you do?

Skip to my Lou, my darling!

Cows in the farmhouse,
Shoo, cows, shoo!
Pigs, ducks, sheep,
And horses, too!

Hens and roosters!
What will we do?

Skip to my Lou, my darling!

Lou, Lou, skip to my Lou!
Lou, Lou, skip to my Lou!
Lou, Lou, skip to my Lou!
Skip to my Lou, my darling!
Whew!

Time to go now.
Toodle-oo!

But we're not sad,
And we're not blue—

Because next week, we're
GOING TO THE ZOO!

Skip to my Lou, my darling!

Adapted by Bill Martin Jr.

Fire! Fire! Said Mrs. McGuire

Illustrated by Nathan Jarvis

"Fire! Fire!" said Mrs. McGuire.

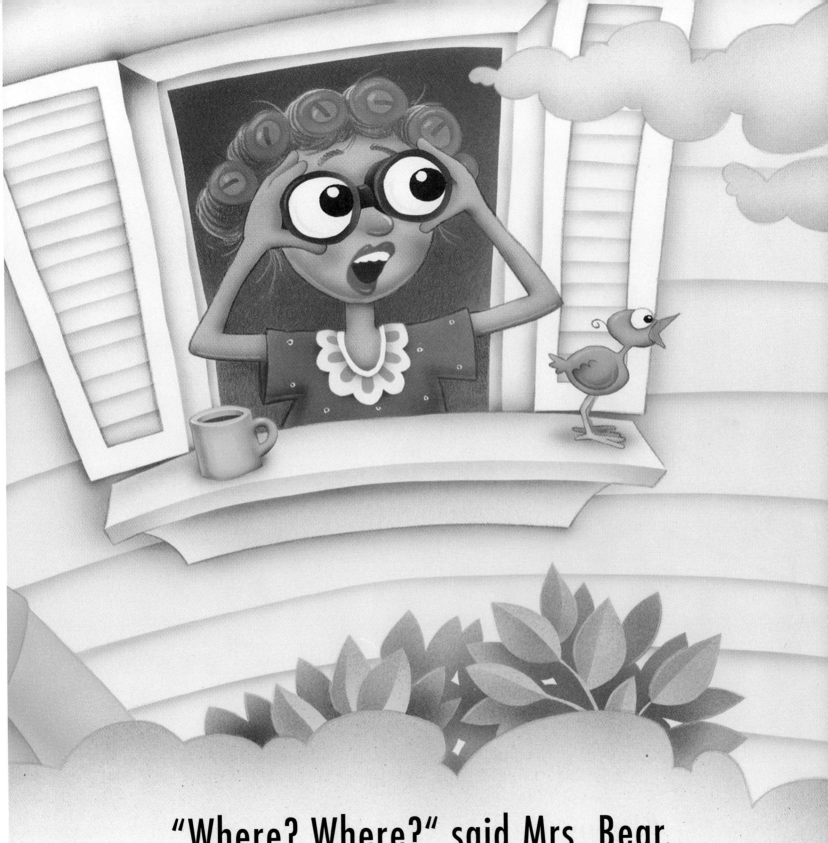

"Where? Where?" said Mrs. Bear.

"Down town!" said Mrs. Brown.

"What floor?" said Mrs. Moore.

"Near the top!" said Mrs. Kopp.

"What a pity!" said Mrs. Kitty.

87

"Help! Help!" said Mrs. Kelp.

"Here I come!" said Mrs. Plumb.

"Water! Water!" said Mrs. Votter.

"Get out of my way!" said Mrs. Lei.

"Let me see!" said Mrs. Chi.

"Break down the door!" said Mrs. Orr.

"Well, I declare!" said Mrs. Wear.

"Oh help us and save us!"
said Mrs. Davis
as she fell down the stairs
with a sack of potatoes.

Acknowledgments

For permission to reprint copyrighted material, grateful acknowledgment
is made to the following sources:

    *William B. Eerdmans Publishing Company: New Friends, True Friends,
Stuck-Like-Glue Friends* by Virginia Kroll, illustrated by Rose Rosely.
© 1994 by Wm. B. Eerdmans Publishing Co.

    Farrar, Straus & Giroux, Inc.: One Gorilla: A Counting Book by Atsuko
Morozumi. Text copyright © 1990 by Mathew Price; illustrations copyright © 1990 by Atsuko Morozumi.

    Harcourt Brace & Company: Fire! Fire! Said Mrs. McGuire by Bill
Martin Jr. Text copyright © 1970 by Harcourt Brace & Company.

Illustration Credits

Ken Spengler, cover art; Maureen George, 4-5; Atsuko Morozumi, 6-31;
Rose Rosely, 32-63; Debbie Tilley, 64-79; Nathan Jarvis, 80-95